THE Bonnie PRINCE CHARLIE

Text by David Ross
Illustrated by Jane Taylor, Genus Art

Reprinted 1999, 2002, 2004

Published by Waverley Books Ltd
New Lanark, Scotland

ISBN 1 902407 00 8

Printed and bound in Slovenia

The Story of Bonnie Prince Charlie

The Siege of Gaeta

"Can I get closer to the fighting? I want to see what's happening."

The red-haired boy's voice rose above the rattle of armour, the neighing of horses, the occasional boom of cannon going off. Young boys are not usually welcome on battlefields, but this boy looked as though he were dressed for warfare. He had his own suit of armour, his own helmet, and a small sword hung by his side – small but real. He had tried his finger on the blade.

The men around him were also dressed for war. They sat on tall horses and looked out from the top of a low hill towards the walls of a town. The name of the town was Gaeta, and their army was besieging it. It was in Italy, and the sun was hot. The boy felt as if he were boiling in his armoured suit, but he was more concerned to see what was happening. He stood up in his stirrups to see better. Far ahead, at the foot of the city walls, men were running to and fro. A puff of smoke came as a gun was fired from inside the walls. The sun sparkled on swords and pikes.

"Please," said the boy. "We are too far away here.

I can't really see what's going on. I want to join the fight."

The men smiled kindly.

"That would not do, your Royal Highness," said one. "We must look after you. This is close enough."

The boy frowned. Then suddenly he jerked the bridle of his horse and set it trotting off, downhill. He heard the men calling out and dug in his spurs. But in a moment or two, a horse drew level with him, and a long arm reached out and caught his rein. His horse was first slowed, then turned. With a sulky face, he was led back up the hill.

"The lad has spirit," murmured one of the men to a friend.

"Yes," was the whispered answer. "Perhaps one day he will do what his father could not."

The boy turned his head sharply, and the whispering stopped.

"It is time to leave," said one of the men.

With many backward glances, the boy allowed himself to be led away from the guns and the soldiers, past fields trampled down by horses and wagons to where a great marquee had been pitched and tables with food and drink stood waiting.

He lived in Italy, in a grand house in Rome. The house was often full of people. Visitors came and went. Sometimes he had to be presented to them. It was from one of these visitors that he first heard two names. One was his own, Charles Edward Stuart. His mother always called him Carlo. The other was Scotland. The man who spoke them both was a tall man with a long face, a big chin and nose, and gentle eyes. He did not wear the usual breeches and silk stockings but long narrow trousers of checked material. The boy knew it was an important meeting because his father was there too, sitting in a big chair. The tall man knelt down, took the boy's hand and kissed it. But he looked closely into the boy's eyes as he did so, as if wondering what he might see.

"This is Doctor Cameron," said his father. "He has come all the way from Scotland to bring us news."

"Prince Charles Edward," said the man in a soft voice. "You will always find me and my clan at your Royal Highness's service and supporting the Stuart cause."

"Thank you," said the boy, giving a little bow as he had been taught to do to important grown-ups. Then his father nodded to the attendants and it was time for him to leave the room.

Through long corridors he raced, on tiled floors, past marble statues, until he reached the rooms of his mother, his beautiful, sparkling-eyed mother, always full of life, whether it was with peals of laughter or storms of tears. Words he had often heard but never listened to were singing in his head.

"Mother," he said. "What is the Stuart cause? And where is Scotland? And what is a clan?"

She took his hands in hers, her face serious for once.

"You know all that," she said.

"Not really," protested the boy.

"Well, it is very simple. Scotland is a country far away, a cold, windy country where the sun hardly ever shines. Brrr," she pretended to shiver, and he smiled. "Next to it is the country of England. Your father should be the king of Scotland and England. That is the Stuart cause. Stuart is the name of his family. His father – your grandfather – was their king, but they wickedly drove him out and made someone else the king instead. And so we live here in Rome, under the protection of the pope, as poor as church mice, when we should be in a great palace in London."

"Is London in Scotland?"

"No, in England. But it is in Scotland especially that we still have friends who will help us to return. They are the clans, who live in the mountains and on the islands – brave warriors. Your father went there once but had to come back again. The time was not right. But soon, with the help of soldiers from our cousin, the king of Spain, we will chase away that other king, who calls himself King George, and your father will be king again. And you" – she pulled him

closer to her – "One day you will be king too. King Charles the Third of England, Ireland and Scotland. Do you know what they say there? 'Hurrah! God Save the King!'"

"But," said the boy, "this is our home. I like it here. Why does my papa want to go to that cold place?"

"Because he is its rightful king. You must never forget that."

Charles Edward never did forget that. He was determined to be a soldier. He knew that a soldier must be able to march, and he took long walks. He practised sword-fighting with his fencing master. He rode his horse every day. He was growing up to be a strong, handsome boy. And, as he grew older, he learned more about who he was and why that strange, cold country called Scotland was so important to his family.

The Seven Men of Moidart

Eleven years after he had visited the siege of Gaeta, Prince Charles Edward was a man of twenty-four. He was no longer in Rome. He was by the seashore in France, waiting for a ship that would take him to Scotland. It was his own idea. There was no great French or Spanish army to sail with him and help him win back the crowns of Scotland and England for his father and himself. He had two ships, a chest of borrowed money and seven hundred men. In the summer of 1745 they set off. But the bigger of the ships, the *Elizabeth,* with all the fighting men, was stopped by a British warship as it approached the coast of England. There was a battle, and the *Elizabeth* was so badly hit that it had to struggle back to France. Charles Edward landed in Scotland, on the island of Eriskay, on the 23rd of July. One of the first people the prince met advised him to go home again.

"I have come home," said the prince, proudly.

Two days later they came to the mainland. He had only seven companions – one was English, four were Irish, two were Scots – they became known as the Seven Men of Moidart.

Soon it became known among the people of the West Highlands that the prince had come. We still have clans today, but at that time, the clan people still obeyed their clan chief. If the chief of Clan Cameron would fight for Prince Charles Edward, so would all the able-bodied Cameron men. If he did not, they would not. And the Cameron chief, Donald of Lochiel, did not want to fight. He did not think the prince could win.

"My father always told me that Cameron of Lochiel was his greatest friend," said the prince, "but if I must fight without you, I will, and you can sit in your house and read in the newspapers about what happens to me."

This roused the chief. "I will come out for you," he promised. With Lochiel to support him, many others also gathered. But others, whose help he had hoped for, would not give it.

By the 19th of August, at Glenfinnan, near Fort William, his army gathered. The Duke of Atholl had come across the mountains with his men, and he raised the royal standard of the Stuarts here. James the Third of England and Eighth of Scotland was proclaimed king, and Prince Charles Edward as his regent. The government far away in London now knew that the prince had come. A huge reward was offered to anyone who captured him. It was worth more than a million pounds in today's money.

Without delay, the prince's army set off. It marched to Perth and from there to Edinburgh. The London government had by now assembled an army to fight him, led by General Sir John Cope, but they had not yet found the prince and his Highlanders. On the 17th of September, the Jacobite army came in sight of Edinburgh. The soldiers who were defending the city ran away, leaving only the castle guarded. The gates of the city were opened, and Prince Charles walked in. The horrified townspeople waited in fear and trembling, but the army was on its best behaviour.

"The Highlanders pay cheerfully for what they get," wrote one citizen with relief.

Prince Charles Edward felt very pleased. His seven men were now an army and he was already in Edinburgh's royal palace of Holyrood. News came that the army of the London government was close at hand, and on September 21st, the prince and his men marched out of Edinburgh for their first battle. The prince wanted to lead the charge himself, but the clan chiefs refused to allow it. They knew that if he should be killed, the Stuart cause would be lost.

It was over in a few minutes. Sir John Cope's men did not stay to face the screaming Highlanders with their long swords. After a few shots, they ran away. Sir John rode all the way to Berwick on Tweed without stopping. People still sing a rude song about him.

"Hey, Johnnie Cope, are ye walking yet?
And are your drums a-beating yet?
If ye were walking, I wad wait
To gang to the coals in the morning."

Prince Charles Edward felt even more pleased. It had not been much of a battle, but he had won it. Many more men came from the Highlands to join his army. Government troops still held Edinburgh Castle, but Prince Charles Edward did not try to force them out. It was not enough for him to have Scotland. He was determined to lead his army into England.

The Advance into England

On the 31st of October, as winter was coming on, Charles Edward and his army set off on the way south to England. He hoped that many Englishmen would join him and fight for the Stuart cause. Indeed, if enough people joined him, perhaps King George would run away and there need be no great battle. By 30th November they had got as far as Manchester, but hardly anyone had joined the prince's army. The English people watched them go by, but they did not cheer. There were none of the "Hurrahs!" that his mother had talked about long ago in Rome.

Charles Edward was sure he would win. His advisers were worried. They realised that the English people did not want to have the Stuart kings back. And they knew that a large army would soon be brought out against them. This army would have cannons and modern guns, as well as more men than the Prince's army. And the English were assembling two other armies. They could not fight against so many. Although they were only a few days' march away from London, they would not go any further. They told the Prince that he must retreat.

He was furiously angry. Having come so far, he did not want to give up. He had been writing letters to his father, making plans for a grand entry into London. Now, like the men at Gaeta, they were making him go away. He raged and stormed. But the chiefs would not change their minds.

"Come back to Scotland," they said. "We will not give up the fight. We will find more men and return again."

On Friday the 6th of December, the Prince's army turned back. But as long as he lived, Prince Charles Edward believed that, if they had gone on, he would have captured London, and the crown of England.

THE RETREAT

Two English generals followed the Highland army as it headed North again. It was a dreary march through wet and cold winter weather. Prince Charles Edward was in a bad temper all the time. When he returned to Scotland, he found that some French soldiers had been sent to help him. But the English army was close behind. Charles Edward and his men were at Stirling, whose castle – like Edinburgh – was occupied by soldiers loyal to King George. On the 17th of January, 1746, there was a battle at Falkirk. Prince Charles Edward's men won the day, but the English army was not destroyed, and the Duke of Cumberland was sent to take command of it.

The Prince wanted to stay in Edinburgh, but the chiefs once again wanted to retreat. It was now the middle of winter, and their men were hungry and weary. They wanted to go home, and to return to fight in the Spring. Unwillingly, the Prince went with the Highlanders to Inverness, reaching it on 18th February.

But the Duke of Cumberland did not wait for the Highlanders to attack again in the Spring. Slowly his

army in their red coats plodded northwards, with their muskets and ammunition, and cannons lumbering behind, pulled by teams of horses.

This Duke, whose name was William, was the second son of King George. He was almost the same age as Prince Charles Edward. But he had been taught how to be a general. He knew much more about fighting battles than Prince Charles did. On April 15th, the day of his 25th birthday, his army arrived at Nairn. Knowing the English soldiers would be celebrating the Duke's birthday, the Highlanders planned a surprise attack by night.

But it did not work. Daylight came when they were still two miles away from the enemy. Any chance of arriving unseen was gone. Wearily, the Highlanders trudged uphill on to a ridge called Drumossie Moor, near Culloden House.

Later on that same day, the battle took place. Nine thousand government troops faced half as many Highlanders. The Duke of Cumberland ordered the cannons to be fired, and the cannon balls tore through the ranks of the Prince's army. The Highlanders charged, but they could not break the ranks of the redcoats. In a short time more than a thousand of the Prince's men lay dead. Many more, including Cameron of Lochiel, were wounded. The battle was lost.

After Culloden – The Prince in the Heather

With the battle of Culloden the Stuart cause was lost forever. The Prince, and the men who had fought for him, were on the run. The Duke of Cumberland and his army stayed in the Highlands, burning houses and killing many people. The Highland people called him "The Butcher". Above all, the redcoats were looking for Charles Edward. The huge reward was still on offer. As he wandered through the Highlands and the Western Isles, many people knew where he could be found. But nobody told. Around the end of June he was on the island of South Uist when a government ship suddenly arrived.

A young woman named Flora MacDonald rescued him, by dressing him in the clothes of her maid, a big Irish girl called Betty Burke. In a small boat Charles Edward and Flora MacDonald sailed across the stormy sea to Skye, and then had to pass through several inspections by government soldiers. Flora was arrested when her part in saving the Prince was discovered, and she was sent to prison for a year. But even those who did not support the Stuart cause

respected her bravery. The grateful Prince gave her a lock of his hair.

Charles Edward continued to lead a hunted life, often sleeping in the heather, but never abandoned by his friends. At last, by arrangement with the King of France, a French ship came to carry him away from Scotland. He left from almost the same place where he had first landed. Cameron of Lochiel and more than a hundred others went with him.

Despite his defeat, Charles Edward was keen to try again. He believed he had been so near success, and he asked the King of France for twenty thousand men, to invade England. But the King refused. The Stuart cause was lost.

Charles Edward lived on for a long time. He never returned to Scotland, though he once went to London in disguise, to view the city where he had hoped to see his father and himself reign as kings, and which he had come so close to capturing in 1745. After his father died, he called himself King Charles the Third, but very few supporters were left to cry "Hurrah! God Save the King." The memory of his bold attempt to win the throne still lives on, in the sad and beautiful Jacobite songs of Scotland:

Sweet the laverock's note, and lang,
Lilting wildly up the glen;
But for me he sings ae sang:
"Will ye no' come back again?"